THE NEW IQ TEST

THE NEW IQ TEST

PHILIP J. CARTER
AND KENNETH A. RUSSELL

JOINT EDITORS OF THE
MENSA UK PUZZLE GROUP JOURNAL

WARD LOCK

A WARD LOCK BOOK

First published in the UK 1994
by Ward Lock
Wellington House
125 Strand
London
WC2R 0BB

A Cassell Imprint

Reprinted 1995 (twice)

Distributed in the United States
by Sterling Publishing Co., Inc.
387 Park Avenue South, New York, NY 10016-8810

Distributed in Australia
by Capricorn Link (Australia) Pty Ltd
2/13 Carrington Road, Castle Hill NSW 2154

A British Library Cataloguing in Publication Data block for this book
is available from the British Library

ISBN 0-7063-7229-8

Design and Typesetting by Ben Cracknell
Printed and bound in Great Britain by
Cox & Wyman Ltd, Reading, Berkshire

Contents

Acknowledgements

The authors are greatly indebted to their wives, both named Barbara, who, as well as supporting them enthusiastically in writing this book, have also contributed in compiling and checking the manuscript. The authors also wish to thank Lynn Moore for typing the final manuscript.

About the Authors

Kenneth Russell is a London surveyor and is also the Puzzle Editor of MENSA, the high IQ society.

Philip Carter is an engineering estimator and also a Yorkshire JP. He is editor of *Enigmasig* the MENSA Special Interest Puzzle Group.

Introduction

The letters IQ stand for Intelligence Quotient. Intelligence can be defined as the ability to respond adaptively to novel situations, while quotient is the number of times that one number will divide into another.

The measured IQ of children is equal to mental age divided by actual (chronological) age. For example, if a child of eight obtains a score expected of a ten-year-old, he or she will have a measured IQ of 125. This is calculated in the following way:

$$\frac{\text{MENTAL AGE}}{\text{CHRONOLOGICAL AGE}} \times 100 = \text{IQ}$$

Therefore $\frac{10}{8} \times 100 = 125 \text{ IQ}$

This method of calculating IQ does not apply to adults because beyond the age of 18 there is little or no improvement in mental development. Adults, therefore, have to be judged on an IQ test in which the average score is 100. The results are graded above and below this norm according to known test scores.

Based on the Cattell scale of intelligence, the population can be split roughly into three main groups: 50 per cent would have an IQ between 90 and 110, 25 per cent would be above 110 and 25 per cent would be below 90. On the

Cattell scale the qualifying level for Mensa is 148, which puts the applicant in the top 2 per cent of the population.

The tests that have been compiled for this book have not been standardized, so an actual IQ assessment cannot be given. However, at the end of each test there is a guide to assesssing your performance and at the end of each complete test (numbered 1, 2, 3 and 4) there is a total score guide for the test.

The tests in this book are intended as valuable practice for readers who may have to take an IQ test in the future and they will also help to increase your vocabulary and to develop your powers of calculation and logical reasoning.

Instructions

There are four complete tests, numbered 1, 2, 3 and 4, and each test contains 10 parts, numbered with Roman numerals.

You have limited time in which to complete the tests, so keep strictly to the time limit, because this could affect your score, and work as quickly as possible.

Do not spend too much time on any one question. If you are in doubt, leave it and return to it using any time remaining. If you do not know an answer have an intuitive guess – this may well be right.

TEST ONE

Test One

Part I is a series of 20 questions designed to test your ability in collecting together objects or ideas that belong to a set or that have some common attribute. To make this classification simpler we have put together a series of words, and you have to spot the 'odd one out'. There are five words and only four of them have a common theme; underline the <u>odd one</u>.

Example: bag, basket, <u>hat</u>, pocket, bucket
Answer: <u>hat</u>, the other four are used for carrying things

You have 10 minutes to complete the 20 questions.

Each correct answer scores one point.

8 - 10	AVERAGE
11 - 13	GOOD
14 - 16	VERY GOOD
17 - 20	EXCEPTIONAL

1. cancel, change, repeal, rescind, revoke
2. gamble, brave, hazard, dash, venture
3. meek, sycophantic, servile, quiet, fawning
4. cleaver, bayonet, mace, machete, dagger
5. inflame, sparkle, scintillate, shine, spangle
6. buck, bull, stag, jack, hind
7. vulgar, blunt, coarse, oafish, unrefined
8. wild, frenetic, frantic, hysterical, excessive
9. facet, appearance, aspect, feature, trait
10. pavilion, terrace, gazebo, belvedere, summer-house
11. concurrent, sporadic, irregular, intermittent, occasional
12. axiom, tenet, precept, formula, creed
13. emotional, avid, ardent, fervent, impassioned
14. cognizance, serendipity, perception, awareness, discernment
15. treadmill, lathe, unicycle, piston, sheave
16. intermission, recess, respite, adjournment, interstice
17. hoard, offertory, accumulation, stockpile, assemblage
18. rhomboid, isosceles, rectangle, rhombus, trapezium
19. elaborate, harangue, expatiate, dilate, expound
20. beige, mocha, cinnabar, sepia, umber

Test One

PART II

Part II is a series of 20 questions designed to test your knowledge of language and your ability to spot words that have the same meaning. We have grouped together five words, and from them you have to underline the <u>word</u> that means the same as or has the closest meaning to the KEY word.

Example: ANGULAR (blunt, stiff, abrupt, <u>branching</u>, cornered)
Answer: <u>branching</u> is the word closest in meaning to the KEY word, ANGULAR

You have 10 minutes to complete the 20 questions.

Each correct answer scores one point.

8 - 10	AVERAGE
11 - 13	GOOD
14 - 16	VERY GOOD
17 - 20	EXCEPTIONAL

1. FRAUD (probity, duplicity, crime, craft, treachery)
2. PALATE (fair, taste, dish, satiate, prepare)
3. CRUST (pastry, pie, shell, crisp, wrinkle)
4. TRIFLING (dallying, stealing, minuscule, foxy, slipping)
5. GUILEFUL (dishonest, wrong, sly, rueful, slipshod)
6. COMPATRIOT (ally, countryman, friend, soldier, colleague)
7. INTUITION (craft, titillation, perception, invasion, concern)
8. INTRANSIGENT (compromising, crossing, involution, tough, silent)
9. DOUBTFUL (wrong, probable, possible, indeterminate, never)
10. INSULAR (silent, restrained, warm, closed, worldly)
11. SILVER (argent, teal, oyster, dove, nankeen)
12. GRISLY (tough, horrid, rough, harmful, stunning)
13. TRINKET (piece, bagatelle, object, braid, blunder)
14. DISARMING (stripping, limiting, likeable, confusing, introvert)
15. SUPERCILIOUS (superior, clever, sarcastic, haughty, extreme)
16. INTEMPERATE (weak, disciplined, excessive, lucid, subdued)
17. LOCUTION (idiom, academy, situation, sound, words)
18. INSURGENT (hopeless, student, rebel, guarantor, cleaner)
19. TRENCHANT (caustic, heavy, steady, fixed, stylish)
20. AEGIS (alliance, patronage, antipathy, study, system)

Part III is a series of 20 questions designed to test your knowledge of language and your ability to visualize opposite meanings quickly. We have grouped together five words and from them you have to underline the <u>word</u> that means the opposite or is as nearly as possible opposite in meaning to the KEY word.

Example: CARELESS (exact, <u>heedful</u>, strict, anxious, dutiful)
Answer: <u>heedful</u> is the word that means the opposite of the
              KEY word CARELESS

You have 10 minutes to complete the 20 questions.

Each correct answer scores one point.

8 - 10	AVERAGE
11 - 13	GOOD
14 - 16	VERY GOOD
17 - 20	EXCEPTIONAL

1. VIGOUR (health, frailty, disgrace, negligence, failure)
2. DEPRAVED (lucky, moral, prosperous, enhanced, great)
3. MAXIMUM (scarcest, shortest, apogee, lowest, gradual)
4. SACRILEGE (reverence, profanity, glowing, good, uniformity)
5. AROMATIC (tart, disagreeable, sour, oppressive, odorous)
6. MUSTY (clean, expensive, fine, sprited, fresh)
7. PUNGENT (mild, lax, sour, brawny, calm)
8. DISCIPLE (agnostic, tutor, neophyte, figurehead, manager)
9. FREQUENT (avoid, depend, endow, enjoy, dispirit)
10. BOORISH (genteel, happy, quiet, simple, reduced)
11. CONVEX (full, indented, protuberant, flat, secret)
12. LUXURY (treachery, comfort, duplicity, sadness, austerity)
13. PRACTISED (unsound, theoretical, calculated, inferior, incompetent)
14. PROPEL (shove, check, hide, hesitate, summarize)
15. INTIMACY (anger, aloofness, fraternization, disgust, fear)
16. GLUT (satiate, paucity, loose, pallid, empty)
17. SALVATION (absolution, perdition, prohibition, envy, dismay)
18. PROSAIC (spoken, indelicate, likely, exciting, flat)
19. MERCURIAL (weak, reliable, small, flighty, cruel)
20. HIDEBOUND (tolerant, appealing, free, showy, resolved)

Test One
PART IV

Part IV is a series of 20 questions designed to test your ability to visualize relationships between various objects and ideas. We have grouped together five words, one of which will pair up with the KEY word to produce a similar relationship to the two-word example. Underline the word that is appropriate.

Example: TIRED is to work as
 HAPPY is to (sleep, rest, success, exercise, eating)
Answer: success has a similar relationship to HAPPY as work has to TIRED

You have 10 minutes to complete the 20 questions.

Each correct answer scores one point.

8 - 10 AVERAGE 11 - 13 GOOD
14 - 16 VERY GOOD 17 - 20 EXCEPTIONAL

ANALOGY

1. VOLT is to electricity as
 WATT is to (power, heat, motion, frequency, pressure)
2. CUB is to bear as
 PUP is to (elephant, rabbit, ass, otter, seal)
3. PIAZZA is to Italy as
 PLAZA is to (Portugal, Morocco, France, Spain, Greece)
4. CRAB is to apple as
 KIWI is to (bird, New Zealand, flight, fruit, china)

5. CADDY is to tea as
   CASKET is to (plants, perfume, gold, cargo, valuables)
6. PASSIONATE is to unbridled as
   GIDDY is to (hasty, madcap, unreasonable, disorderly, heated)
7. LIAISON is to affair as
   INFATUATION is to (secret, platonic, dalliance, passion, gesture)
8. VESTRY is to church as
   DISPENSARY is to (school, hospital, monastery, laboratory, ship)
9. NOTICE is to observe as
   PROPHECY is to (prophet, prediction, story, truth, ideas)
10. RANCOUR is to ranker as
    FRAYS is to (frieze, prays, frail, phrase, frees)
11. VENERATE is to worship as
    EXTOL is to (joy, glorify, recommend, homage, compliment)
12. MILITANT is to combative as
    PACIFIC is to (hostile, water, ocean, gentle, strange)
13. VIGILANT is to alert as
    VIABLE is to (useful, feasible, hopeless, gentle, active)
14. CHISEL is to cut as
    BROACH is to (hammer, drill, smooth, wrench, saw)
15. PRESTO is to fast as
    VIVACE is to (fast, loud, smoothly, briskly, vigorously)
16. CLAYMORE is to sword as
    BERETTA is to (knife, gun, club, axe, spear)
17. CORNUAL is to horn as
    PANDURATE is to (harp, violin, lyre, oboe, triangle)
18. JADE is to green as
    GARNET is to (yellow, red, brown, orange, blue)
19. RELUCTANT is to keen as
    REMARKABLE is to (usual, striking, evocative, utterance, restrained)
20. FACILE is to maladroit as
    PERVERSE is to (churlish, steady, amiable, correct, foreign)

Test One

Part V is a series of 20 questions designed to test your knowledge of language and your ability to recognize words of similar meanings quickly. There are six words in each question and you have to find a pair of words that have similar meanings. Underline the two words that you believe to be closest in meaning.

Example: walk, run, drive, stroll, fly, sit
Answer: walk and stroll are the two words that are closest in meaning

You have 10 minutes to complete the 20 questions.

Each correct answer scores one point.

8 - 10	AVERAGE
11 - 13	GOOD
14 - 16	VERY GOOD
17 - 20	EXCEPTIONAL

1. develop, injure, headache, illness, migraine, pain
2. smooth, pound, knead, cut, massage, make
3. shave, miss, lady, spinster, person, marriage
4. collect, vouch, propose, taste, certify, devour
5. amend, abet, build, calculate, abide, support
6. drive, deflect, extend, veer, stop, contort
7. changing, active, living, designing, working, torpid
8. happen, trip, find, befall, accept, proper
9. interim, period, interval, meantime, inside, insert
10. words, lyrical, singing, rhapsodic, music, sound
11. finish, cringe, point, recoil, strain, damage
12. snag, compound, hitch, extend, solve, ponder
13. winnow, hero, part, opening, cold, change
14. unpaid, thanks, relevant, lattice, gratis, humour
15. harried, critical, hardline, bold, intransigent, narrow
16. spendthrift, profiteer, profit, gangster, overcharge, charge
17. high, distance, broad, cramped, size, capacious
18. nostrum, operation, attend, regret, posy, elixir
19. exploit, charge, milk, liquid, attest, fondle
20. politician, nuncio, monk, envoy, person, count

Test One

Part VI is a series of 20 questions designed to test your knowledge of language and your ability to recognize words of opposite meanings quickly. There are six words in each question and you have to find a pair of words that have opposite meanings. Underline the two words that you believe to be opposite in meaning.

Example: curved, long, big, small, broad, fat
Answer: big, and small, are the two words in the list that are
          opposite in meaning

You have 10 minutes to complete the 20 questions.

Each correct answer scores one point.

8 - 10	AVERAGE
11 - 13	GOOD
14 - 16	VERY GOOD
17 - 20	EXCEPTIONAL

1. feel, stop, hurry, move, tarry, change
2. civil, parliamentary, military, academic, official, sternly
3. righteous, lament, questionable, selfish, immoral, ready
4. low, prone, long, slow, vertical, pronounced
5. discharge, disjoin, demolish, deter, contract, attach
6. rare, obtuse, clear, idiotic, eulogistic, acceptable
7. reckon, relish, contact, feed, dislike, argue
8. shifty, evil, frank, friendly, sad, expert
9. excessive, changeable, feasible, hopeful, emotional, dejected
10. difficult, strange, incoherent, loud, unique, logical
11. unsuited, sullen, warm, sunny, complete, near
12. widen, secrete, clean, destroy, reveal, accept
13. quiet, misspent, impressed, fruitful, formative, notable
14. flair, blithe, expert, languid, churlish, serious
15. faulty, fateful, worried, favourable, dead, unimportant
16. citizen, general, sergeant, restricted, stopped, lonely
17. quaint, allegorical, excellent, factual, bellicose, overt
18. fair, crude, nasty, genteel, fierce, surly
19. worried, phlegmatic, angry, excited, sagacious, somatic
20. joy, dispute, scorn, choler, renew, limit

Part VII is a series of 20 questions designed to test your ability to find alternative meanings of words quickly You are looking for a word that has the same meaning as one word or phrase in one sense and the same meaning as a different word or phrase in another sense. The dots represent the number of letters in the missing word. Fill in the missing word.

Example: breathes heavily . . . . . . underclothes
Answer: pants

You have 20 minutes to complete the 20 questions.

Each correct answer scores one point.

8 - 10	AVERAGE
11 - 13	GOOD
14 - 16	VERY GOOD
17 - 20	EXCEPTIONAL

DOUBLE MEANINGS

1. young bovine animal .... part of the leg
2. a hole in the ground ... the stone of a fruit
3. to vibrate harshly ... a vessel of glass or earthenware
4. a hollow shape for pouring metal ..... a fungal growth
5. a strong taste or flavour .... to make a ringing, twanging noise
6. strike lightly or gently ... a faucet
7. belonging to me .... an excavation
8. nurture .... the back
9. female deer .... situated at the back
10. walk lightly ...... quick, idle talk
11. a stack of hay .... to wrench or sprain
12. to fix ... a collection
13. an instrument for cotton spinning .... a backless shoe
14. a portable case for arrows ...... to tremble
15. a freshwater fish ..... a land measure of 5 ½ yards
16. to arrange mutually .... public musical entertainment
17. a rounded hill ..... to summon by ringing
18. methodical .... a male hospital attendant
19. to limp .... a stop in activity
20. the art of public speaking .... a small chapel

Test One

PART VIII

Part VIII is a series of 20 questions designed to test your ability at innovation. You are given the first part of the word or phrase, and you have to find the second part. The same second part then becomes the first part of a second word or phrase. The dots represent the number of letters in the missing word. Fill in the missing word.

Example: house . . . . all
Answer: hold

You have 20 minutes to complete the 20 questions.

Each correct answer scores one point.

8 - 10	AVERAGE
11 - 13	GOOD
14 - 16	VERY GOOD
17 - 20	EXCEPTIONAL

DOUBLE WORDS

1. pull .... cast
2. mean .... worn
3. snap .... gun
4. snow .... out
5. school .... friend
6. mast .... line
7. roll .... lace
8. low .... beat
9. buck ..... room
10. wreck ... less
11. corn ... web
12. house ... side
13. fruit .... on
14. ant ... self
15. dust ... ache
16. sting ... on
17. go .. set
18. class .... lot
19. test ... lier
20. pan ... sail

Part IX is a series of 10 culture-free tests designed to test your powers of logical reasoning and understanding of relationships, pattern and design. Study each display of diagrams and select the missing item from the choices given. Study the instructions given to each question.

Example: Which is the odd one out?

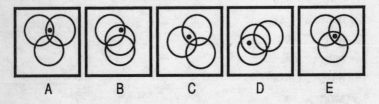

A   B   C   D   E

Answer: E – the dot is in three circles. In the other options it is in only two.

Each correct answer scores two points.

8 - 10	AVERAGE
12 - 14	GOOD
16	VERY GOOD
18 - 20	EXCEPTIONAL

1.

Which of the following continues the above sequence?

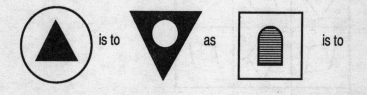

2.

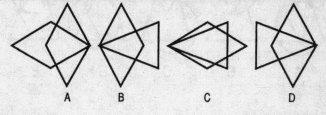

3.

Which of the following continues the above sequence?

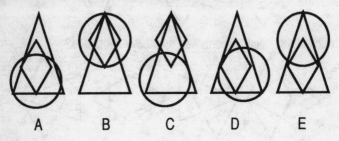

A   B   C   D   E

4. Find the missing tile.

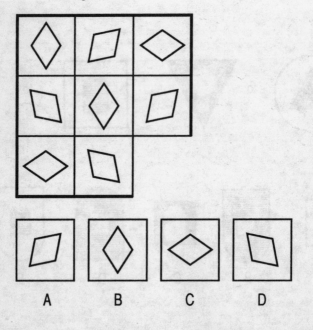

A   B   C   D

5.

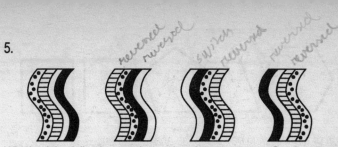

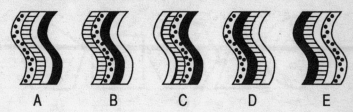

Which of the following continues the above sequence?

A   B   C   D   E

6.

Which of the following continues the above sequence?

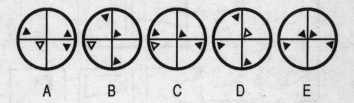

A   B   C   D   E

7.

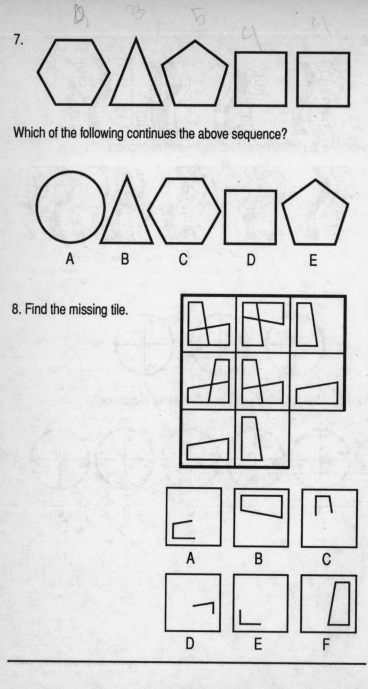

Which of the following continues the above sequence?

A   B   C   D   E

8. Find the missing tile.

A   B   C

D   E   F

9.

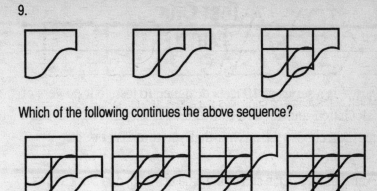

Which of the following continues the above sequence?

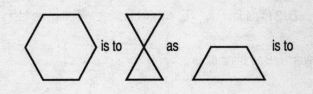

A   B   C   D

10.

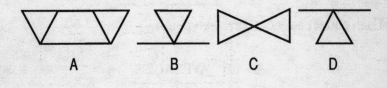

A   B   C   D

Test One
PART X

Part X is a series of 10 tests designed to test your powers of calculation and logic. From the alternatives given in each question choose the answer that you think is correct.

Example: My watch shows the time at 12.25; one clock shows 12.10. The radio announces 12.30, the church clock strikes 12.00, and your watch shows 12.15. The correct time is 12.20. What is the average time, fast or slow, as shown by these timepieces?

A. 2 mins slow   B. 4 mins slow   C. 6 mins slow
D. 2 mins fast   E. 4 mins fast   F. 6 mins fast

Answer: B. 4 mins slow

You have 20 minutes in which to solve the 10 questions.

Each correct answer scores two points.

8 - 10	AVERAGE
12 - 14	GOOD
16	VERY GOOD
18 - 20	EXCEPTIONAL

CALCULATION AND LOGIC

1. How many minutes is it before 12 noon if $1\frac{1}{2}$ hours ago it was twice as many minutes past 8am?

A. 30 mins   B. 35 mins   C. 42 mins   D. 50 mins   E. 56 mins

2. Jim beats Sid at tennis but loses to Alf. Jack usually wins against Sid, sometimes against Jim but never against Alf. Who is the weakest player?

A. Alf   B. Sid   C. Jim   D. Jack

3. What is the value of $2\frac{1}{12} - 1\frac{1}{2} + 3\frac{1}{4}$?

A. $2\frac{7}{8}$ B. $2\frac{17}{24}$ C. $3\frac{1}{6}$ D. $3\frac{1}{4}$ E. $3\frac{5}{6}$

4. Sid and Alf share out the profit on their horse race winnings in the ratio 4:5, and Alf receives £8. What was the total profit which they shared out?

A. £12.60   B. £13.40   C. £14.40   D. £14.80   E. £15.30

5. A man jogs at 6mph over a certain journey and walks back over the same route at 4mph. What is his average speed for the journey?

A. 4.25mph   B. 4.6mph   C. 4.8mph   D. 5mph   E. 5.2mph

6. Out of 100 ladies surveyed, 72 had a white handbag, 85 had black shoes, 58 carried an umbrella and 98 wore a ring. How many ladies at least must have had all four items?

A. 13   B. 14   C. 15   D. 16   E. 17

7. What is the missing number in the third circle?

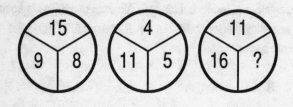

8.   A   B   C   D   E   F   G   H

Which letter is two to the right of the letter, three to the left of the letter immediately to the left of the letter, five to the right of the letter, immediately to the left of the letter D?

9. What is the missing number in the centre of the third cross?

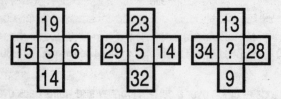

10. Which number is missing from the bottom right-hand square?

8	16	32
36	28	252
72	112	?

Test One

ANSWERS

Part I
1. change 2. dash 3. quiet
4. mace 5. inflame 6. hind 7. blunt
8. excessive 9. appearance
10. terrace 11. concurrent
12. formula 13. emotional
14. serendipity 15. piston
16. interstice 17. offertory
18. isosceles 19. harangue
20. cinnabar

Part II
1. duplicity 2. taste 3. shell
4. minuscule 5. sly 6. countryman
7. perception 8. tough
9. indeterminate 10. closed
11. argent 12. horrid 13. bagatelle
14. likeable 15. haughty
16. excessive 17. idiom 18. rebel
19. caustic 20. patronage

Part III
1. frailty 2. moral 3. lowest
4. reverence 5. odorous 6. fresh
7. mild 8. tutor 9. avoid
10. genteel 11. indented
12. austerity 13. incompetent
14. check 15. aloofness
16. paucity 17. perdition

18. exciting 19. reliable
20. tolerant

Part IV
1. power 2. seal 3. Spain 4. fruit
5. valuables 6. madcap 7. passion
8. hospital 9. prediction
10. phrase 11. glorify 12. gentle
13. feasible 14. drill 15. briskly
16. gun 17. violin 18. red
19. usual 20. amiable

Part V
1. headache, migraine 2. knead,
massage 3. miss, spinster
4. vouch, certify 5. abet, support
6. deflect, veer 7. active, working
8. happen, befall 9. interim,
meantime 10. lyrical, rhapsodic
11. cringe, recoil 12. snag, hitch
13. winnow, part 14. unpaid, gratis
15. hardline, intransigent
16. profiteer, overcharge
17. broad, capacious
18. nostrum, elixir 19. exploit, milk
20. nuncio, envoy

Part VI

1. hurry, tarry 2. civil, military
3. righteous, immoral 4. prone,
vertical 5. disjoin, attach
6. obtuse, clear 7. relish, dislike
8. shifty, frank 9. hopeful, dejected
10. incoherent, logical 11. sullen,
sunny 12. secrete, reveal
13. misspent, fruitful 14. blithe,
churlish 15. fateful, unimportant
16. general, restricted
17. allegorical, factual 18. crude,
genteel 19. phlegmatic, excited
20. joy, choler

Part VII

1. calf 2. pit 3. jar 4. mould 5. tang
6. tap 7. mine 8. rear 9. hind
10. patter 11. rick 12. set 13. mule
14. quiver 15. perch 16. concert
17. knoll 18. orderly 19. halt
20. oratory

Part VIII

1. over 2. time 3. shot 4. drop
5. girl 6. head 7. neck 8. brow
9. board 10. age 11. cob 12. top
13. less 14. her 15. pan 16. ray
17. on 18. mate 19. ate 20. try

Part IX

1. B 2. B 3. E 4. B 5. A 6. C 7. E
8. E 9. B 10. B

Part X

1. D (50 mins) 2. B (Sid)
3. E ($3^5/_6$) 4. C (£14.40)
5. C (4.8mph) 6. A (13) 7. 9 (16 +
11 = 27 ÷ 3 = 9) 8. F 9. 2 (13 + 9
÷ 11 = 2; 34 - 28 ÷ 3 = 2)
10. 2016 (8 x 16 ÷ 4 = 32; 36 x 28
÷ 4 = 252, 72 x 112 ÷ 4 = 2016;
likewise on all vertical columns)

✳ **TOTAL SCORE** ✳

80-100	AVERAGE
101-130	GOOD
131-160	VERY GOOD
161-200	EXCEPTIONAL

TEST TWO

Test Two

Part I is a series of 20 questions designed to test your ability in collecting together objects or ideas that belong to a set or that have some common attribute. To make this classification simpler we have put together a series of words, and you have to spot the 'odd one out'. There are five words and only four of them have a common theme; underline the <u>odd one</u>.

Example: bag, basket, <u>hat</u>, pocket, bucket
Answer: <u>hat</u>, the other four are used for carrying things

You have 10 minutes to complete the 20 questions.

Each correct answer scores one point.

8 - 10	AVERAGE
11 - 13	GOOD
14 - 16	VERY GOOD
17 - 20	EXCEPTIONAL

CLASSIFICATION

1. drain, empty, conduit, sewer, culvert
2. guffaw, growl, chortle, snigger, simper
3. Celtic, Greek, papal, Maltese, pious
4. caricature, burlesque, clown, parody, lampoon
5. Avalon, Elysium, Hades, Valhalla, Utopia
6. leap, frolic, cavort, gambol, rollick
7. shrivel, sully, wizen, wither, shrink
8. plagiarism, rustling, purloining, remitting, pirating
9. gorge, canyon, cliff, ravine, gulch
10. rectify, criticize, remedy, redress, correct
11. busby, biretta, fedora, sabot, mitre
12. glorify, endorse, extol, laud, exalt
13. fife, tambour, oboe, tuba, cornet
14. unassuming, demure, unobtrusive, diffident, tactful
15. minim, clef, crotchet, quaver, semibreve
16. stirrup, girth, flap, pommel, bridle
17. copse, meadow, coppice, thicket, spinney
18. fresco, crown, imperial, royal, foolscap
19. accepted, obliged, beholden, grateful, indebted
20. rose, oriel, tower, lancet, bay

Test Two

PART II

Part II is a series of 20 questions designed to test your knowledge of language and your ability to spot words that have the same meaning. We have grouped together five words, and from them you have to underline the <u>word</u> that means the same as or has the closest meaning to the KEY word.

Example: ANGULAR (blunt, stiff, abrupt, <u>branching</u>, cornered)
Answer: <u>branching</u> is the word closest in meaning to the KEY word, ANGULAR

You have 10 minutes to complete the 20 questions.

Each correct answer scores one point.

8 - 10	AVERAGE
11 - 13	GOOD
14 - 16	VERY GOOD
17 - 20	EXCEPTIONAL

1. PINE (peak, tree, crave, press, worry)
2. LOFTY (large, thin, high, fat, prolonged)
3. WANE (wax, diminish, ashen, rouse, attend)
4. INVALIDATE (counteract, disable, ratify, annul, censure)
5. DESPOIL (mourn, loathe, cheat, divide, loot)
6. LUSTY (bright, sharp, hale, lavish, large)
7. QUAIL (odd, bird, cringe, brawl, agonize)
8. SEPARABLE (apart, severable, split, single, disunited)
9. FATE (alarm, fear, kismet, ego, physiognomy)
10. HYPOTHESIS (promotion, work, sincerity, news, premiss)
11. OPULENT (lavish, extra, indigent, open, harsh)
12. MIGHT (energy, capacity, bravery, speciality, intellect)
13. EQUABLE (serene, unstable, general, brief, predictable)
14. ENTOURAGE (inlet, staff, presence, devotee, whole)
15. PERSONAGE (official, character, employees, portrayal, dignitary)
16. SERAPHIC (beatific, calm, beautiful, well, fair)
17. PROGENY (quantity, relation, skill, descendants, professor)
18. INTERPOSE (mediate, clarify, translate, enquire, add)
19. ABNEGATION (elimination, hatred, renunciation, primeval, failure)
20. PERQUISITE (tenacity, bonus, stamina, fee, remittance)

Test Two

Part III is a series of 20 questions designed to test your knowledge of language and your ability to visualize opposite meanings quickly. We have grouped together five words and from them you have to underline the word that means the opposite or is as nearly as possible opposite in meaning to the KEY word.

Example: CARELESS (exact, heedful, strict, anxious, dutiful)
Answer: heedful is the word that means the opposite of the
          KEY word CARELESS

You have 10 minutes to complete the 20 questions.

Each correct answer scores one point.

8 - 10	AVERAGE
11 - 13	GOOD
14 - 16	VERY GOOD
17 - 20	EXCEPTIONAL

1. SPARSE (scattered, heavy, lavish, expensive, beautiful)
2. FINITE (critical, eternal, terminable, inception, blunt)
3. HAIL (leave, ignore, fine, accost, chop)
4. TANGLE (proceed, solve, tame, extricate, develop)
5. REAR (middle, bow, hind, port, up)
6. ZEALOUS (slow, lonely, apathetic, ancient, venerable)
7. PASTEL (delicate, blank, bright, sweet, urban)
8. CURDLE (disappear, solidify, moderate, dissolve, distance)
9. PARALLEL (round, divergent, curved, wavy, random)
10. GINGERLY (distastefully, masterly, rashly, fastidiously, bravely)
11. NONCHALANT (quick, worried, offhand, memorable, significant)
12. HABITUATED (empty, raw, ingrained, unoccupied, unfamiliar)
13. MANDATORY (shabby, unruly, optional, agreeable, amiable)
14. DOUR (strict, cheerful, active, young, radical)
15. WINDING (narrow, plumb, wide, long, flat)
16. PROSCRIBE (curtail, interdict, allow, betray, extend)
17. RECURRENT (isolated, weakened, strained, free, accepted)
18. PROFLIGATE (chaste, stupid, wealthy, lucrative, worthless)
19. GERMANE (local, unrelated, quick, young, acceptable)
20. MOTLEY (similar, lifeless, smart, handsome, still)

PART IV

Part IV is a series of 20 questions designed to test your ability to visualize relationships between various objects and ideas. We have grouped together five words, one of which will pair up with the KEY word to produce a similar relationship to the two-word example. Underline the _word_ that is appropriate.

Example: TIRED is to work as
HAPPY is to (sleep, rest, <u>success</u>, exercise, eating)

Answer: <u>success</u> has a similar relationship to HAPPY as work has to TIRED

You have 10 minutes to complete the 20 questions.

Each correct answer scores one point.

8 - 10 AVERAGE   11 - 13 GOOD
14 - 16 VERY GOOD   17 - 20 EXCEPTIONAL

ANALOGY

1. TIBIA is to shin as
ULNA is to (leg, arm, thigh, head, neck)
2. ESCUDO is to Portugal as
YEN is to (China, Korea, Thailand, Japan, Vietnam)
3. APOGEE is to perigee as
APHELION is to (perilune, perihelion, epicycle, aposelene, orbit)
4. SANCTUARY is to haven as
RAMPART is to (protection, asylum, refuge, castle, bulwark)

5. ALIENATION is to estrangement as
   PARANOIA is to (ego, persecution, inhibition, persona, behaviour)
6. ABDUCTION is to kidnapping as
   LARCENY is to (crime, blackmail, sin, felony, theft)
7. LATTICE is to window as
   MANSARD is to (door, roof, house, parapet, gambrel)
8. FORFEIT is to surrender as
   REMIT is to (confiscate, exempt, cancel, inflict, reprieve)
9. CONVOY is to ships as
   DEPUTATION is to (writers, faction, politicians, representatives, voters)
10. -GRAM is to writing as
   -LING is to (wrong, speech, young, previous, part)
11. NOSTALGIA is to wistful as
   THOUGHTFUL is to (prodigal, solicitous, sad, quiet, selfish)
12. GALLEY is to oars as
   PACKET is to (ship, sea, rudder, engine, crew)
13. INDISCREET is to imprudent as
   INDISPOSED is to (reluctant, crucial, clear, wealthy, concerned)
14. JEZEBEL is to femme fatale as
   LOLITA is to (sylph, nymphet, cocotte, concubine, damsel)
15. HIGHBROW is to cultivated as
   SUAVE is to (stylish, urbane, broad-minded, elegant, clover)
16. PARKIN is to cake as
   FLAPJACK is to (bun, pancake, pastry, biscuit, bread)
17. LEISURELY is to unhurried as
   TARDY is to (sour, dawdle, dim, sluggish, prolonged)
18. PEDICEL is to stalk as
   COROLLA is to (leaves, stigma, stamen, spike, petals)
19. VITRO is to glass as
   LIGNO is to (rock, marble, metal, grass, wood)
20. ZOOPHOBIA is to animals as
   ICHTHYOPHOBIA is to (dogs, birds, cats, mice, fish)

Test Two

Part V is a series of 20 questions designed to test your knowledge of language and your ability to recognize words of similar meanings quickly. There are six words in each question and you have to find a pair of words that have similar meanings. Underline the two words that you believe to be closest in meaning.

Example: walk, run, drive, stroll, fly, sit

Answer: walk and stroll are the two words that are closest in meaning

You have 10 minutes to complete the 20 questions.

Each correct answer scores one point.

8 - 10	AVERAGE
11 - 13	GOOD
14 - 16	VERY GOOD
17 - 20	EXCEPTIONAL

1. hold, rear, follow, derive, foster, breed
2. connect, juncture, period, visit, moment, place
3. stereotype, dovecote, pigeonhole, bare, charge, confuse
4. virtuoso, magnate, ambassador, plutocrat, magistrate, captain
5. deity, king, being, colleague, lover, idol
6. little, nothing, number, something, cipher, everything
7. revere, ride, venerate, scorn, gain, extend
8. cheap, homespun, cosy, yarn, quaint, rustic
9. sail, row, charge, rank, comply, settle
10. glum, mire, search, mess, morass, revelry
11. garment, relent, vestige, object, cloister, remnant
12. cruise, salient, address, saline, important, auction
13. convivial, hungry, gregarious, satisfied, charming, hopeless
14. sceptic, zealot, fanatic, enemy, hunter, charmer
15. sidelong, thin, oblique, angular, thick, deflect
16. evil, omen, patriarch, presage, attend, begin
17. overt, eventual, ulterior, basic, covert, motive
18. grow, gourmet, taste, epicure, chef, advocate
19. automobile, divorce, option, fiat, decree, drive
20. overweight, obdurate, docile, stubborn, comply, angry

Test Two

Part VI is a series of 20 questions designed to test your knowledge of language and your ability to recognize words of opposite meanings quickly. There are six words in each question and you have to find a pair of words that have opposite meanings. Underline the <u>two words</u> that you believe to be opposite in meaning.

Example: curved, long, <u>big</u>, <u>small</u>, broad, fat
Answer   <u>big</u> and <u>small</u> are the two words in the list that are
           opposite in meaning

You have 10 minutes to complete the 20 questions.

Each correct answer scores one point.

8 - 10	AVERAGE
11 - 13	GOOD
14 - 16	VERY GOOD
17 - 20	EXCEPTIONAL

1. apply, desert, validate, oasis, rescue, demote
2. similar, opposite, amended, cancelled, near, varying
3. substantial, tall, minuscule, magnitude, enormous, proportion
4. grow, fasten, bloat, sink, stay, deflate
5. catty, feline, pleasant, lonely, unwell, sorry
6. smooth, evasive, shameful, noisy, candid, shunned
7. honest, adorable, beautiful, funny, queer, obnoxious
8. narrow, unusual, unquestionable, main, traditional, twisted
9. liberal, conservative, republican, totalitarian, parliamentarian, democratic
10. slapdash, dangerous, pernickety, plumb, perpetual, paradoxical
11. altering, taxing, vindicating, freeing, effortless, remitting
12. facetious, caesious, ostentatious, keen, modest, abstentious
13. wistful, loved, wrathful, strained, mindful, contented
14. cede, bile, roster, bias, rancour, tolerance
15. procrastinate, conceal, expedite, hide, expel, acknowledge
16. careful, facilitate, maladroit, frustrate, aspect, show
17. hopeful, false, cool, resilient, sharp, sensitive
18. living, fatal, playful, fresh, innocuous, beginning
19. bitter, toxic, unwanted, salubrious, necessary, kind
20. worsen, loosen, fix, ameliorate, subjugate, wrangle

Test Two

Part VII is a series of 20 questions designed to test your ability to find alternative meanings of words quickly You are looking for a word that has the same meaning as one word or phrase in one sense and the same meaning as a different word or phrase in another sense. The dots represent the number of letters in the missing word. Fill in the missing word.

Example: breathes heavily . . . . . underclothes
Answer: pants

You have 20 minutes to complete the 20 questions.

Each correct answer scores one point.

8 - 10	AVERAGE
11 - 13	GOOD
14 - 16	VERY GOOD
17 - 20	EXCEPTIONAL

1. a military station . . . . an upright pole
2. remainder . . . . repose
3. to cause to lean . . . the point
4. to climb a ladder . . . . . the dish of a balance
5. a fixed point in time . . . . a type of fruit
6. a form taken by a verb . . . . . under emotional stress
7. in good or right manner . . . . a water hole
8. a conserve of fruit . . . to squeeze
9. to fish with rod and line . . . . . a corner
10. to deceive . . . to recline
11. to retreat . . . . . . to restore to a former possessor
12. the prolonged bark of a dog . . . reddish-brown
13. a large receptacle . . . . . . a sharp rejoinder
14. a pale brownish or reddish-yellow colour . . . . . . land left uncultivated
15. complete, total . . . . . to give forth audibly
16. a facetious fellow . . . shake up and down
17. a type of horse . . . . . a species of falcon
18. the projecting side of a grate . . . an elf
19. a package . . . . evil, mischief, calamity
20. a clasp or buckle . . . . an expression of sudden pain

PART VIII

Part VIII is a series of 20 questions designed to test your ability at innovation. You are given the first part of the word or phrase, and you have to find the second part. The same second part then becomes the first part of a second word or phrase. The dots represent the number of letters in the missing word. Fill in the missing word.

Example: house . . . . all
Answer: hold

You have 20 minutes to complete the 20 questions.

Each correct answer scores one point.

8 - 10	AVERAGE
11 - 13	GOOD
14 - 16	VERY GOOD
17 - 20	EXCEPTIONAL

DOUBLE WORDS

1. sand ... age
2. swim .... able
3. log .... keeper
4. whole .... how
5. fair ... side
6. cub .. self
7. mud .... age
8. past .. deal
9. red .... work
10. want .. ward
11. step ... net
12. can ... not
13. vamp ... land
14. weather ..... read
15. visit ... hem
16. ox ... let
17. sex ... sure
18. lode .... ring
19. dim ... her
20. quiet .. her

Test Two

PART IX

Part IX is a series of 10 culture-free tests designed to test your powers of logical reasoning and understanding of relationships, pattern and design. Study each display of diagrams and select the missing item from the choices given. Study the instructions given to each question.

Example: Which is the odd one out?

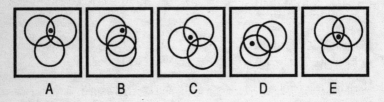

A   B   C   D   E

Answer: E – the dot is in three circles. In the other options it is in only two.

Each correct answer scores two points.

8 - 10	AVERAGE
12 - 14	GOOD
16	VERY GOOD
18 - 20	EXCEPTIONAL

1.

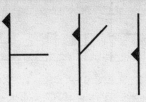

Which of the following continues the above sequence?

A B C D E

2. Which of the following belongs at the top of the pyramid?

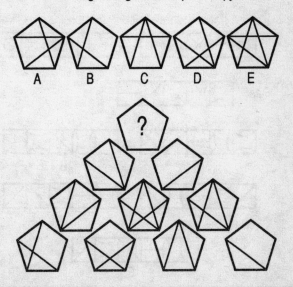

3.

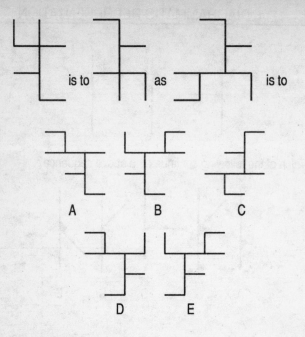

is to ... as ... is to

A   B   C

D   E

4.

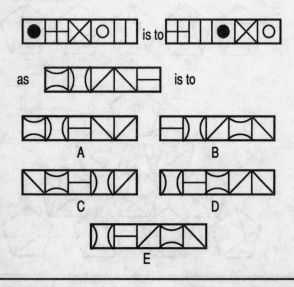

is to ... as ... is to

A

B

C

D

E

5.

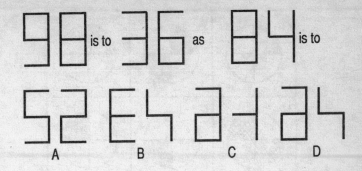

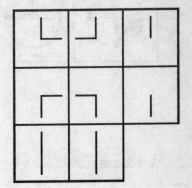

6. Find the missing tile.

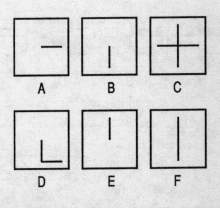

7. Which is the odd one out?

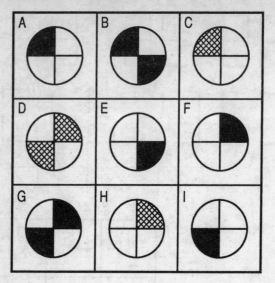

8. Which is the odd one out?

A   B   C   D   E

9.

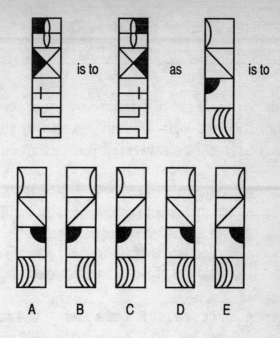

is to ... as ... is to

A B C D E

10. Find the missing tile.

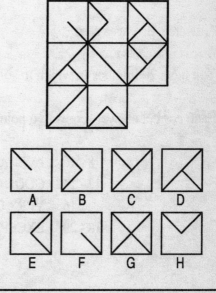

A B C D

E F G H

Test Two

Part X is a series of 10 tests designed to test your powers of calculation and logic. From the alternatives given in each question choose the answer that you think is correct.

Example: My watch shows the time at 12.25; one clock shows 12.10. The radio announces 12.30, the church clock strikes 12.00, and your watch shows 12.15. The correct time is 12.20. What is the average time, fast or slow, as shown by these timepieces?

A. 2 mins slow   B. 4 mins slow   C. 6 mins slow

D. 2 mins fast   E. 4 mins fast   F. 6 mins fast

Answer: B. 4 mins slow

You have 20 minutes in which to solve the 10 questions.

Each correct answer scores two points.

8 - 10	AVERAGE
12 - 14	GOOD
16	VERY GOOD
18 - 20	EXCEPTIONAL

1. During the morning a newsagent sold two copies of one magazine and five copies of a newspaper for a total of £5. During the afternoon he sold five copies of the same magazine and two copies of the same newspaper for a total of £6.20. What is the cost of one newspaper?

A. £0.50   B. £0.60   C. £0.80   D. £0.85   E. £0.90

2. Jim, Sid, Alf, Jack and George were batting for the same team. Jack scored more than Alf; Sid scored more than Jack; Alf scored more than Jim; and George scored less than Sid. Which of the following conclusions is, therefore, proved to be true?

A. Jack scored more than Jim but less than Alf.
B. Jack scored less than Jim and Sid.
C. Jack outscored Jim by more than he outscored Alf.
D. George scored more than Alf.
E. None of these conclusions is proved to be true.

3. What number should replace the question mark?

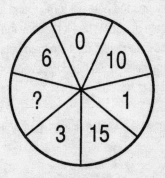

4. How many minutes before 12 noon is it if one hour ago it was five times as many minutes past 9am?

A. 15 mins   B. 18 mins   C. 20 mins   D. 25 mins   E. 35 mins

5.   A   B   C   D   E   F   G   H

Which letter is immediately to the right of the letter, two to the left of the letter immediately to the left of the letter two to the right of the letter four to the left of the letter immediately to the left of the letter G?

6. Sid has £400 to spend. He spends $\frac{2}{5}$ of the £400 on electrical goods, 0.425 of the £400 on clothes and writes out a cheque for £120 for a new watch. What is his financial situation at the end of the day?

A. Plus £40   B. Plus £20   C. Level   D. Minus £20   E. Minus £50

7. A man is walking his dog on the lead towards home at a steady 5mph. When they are 4 miles from home the man lets his dog off the lead. The dog immediately runs off towards home at 8mph. When the dog reaches the house it turns round and runs back to the man at the same speed. When it reaches the man it turns back for the house. This is repeated until the man gets home and lets in the dog. How many miles does the dog cover from being let off the lead to being let in the house?

A. 4.6 miles   B. 4.8 miles   C. 5.8 miles   D. 6.4 miles   E. 6.8 miles

8. A train travelling at a speed of 75mph enters a tunnel $3\frac{1}{2}$ miles long. The train is $\frac{1}{4}$ mile long. How long does it take for all of the train to pass through the tunnel from the moment the front enters to the moment the rear emerges?

A. 2.2 mins   B. 2.5 mins   C. 3 mins   D. 3.2 mins   E. 3.5 mins

9. What is the next number in this sequence?

   0, 1, 1, 3, 6, 9, 27, 31, X

10. What is the value of $2\frac{1}{2} \div \frac{5}{7}$?

Test Two

ANSWERS

Part I

1. drain 2. growl 3. pious 4. clown
5. Hades 6. leap 7. sully
8. remitting 9 . cliff 10. criticize
11. sabot 12. endorse
13. tambour 14. tactful 15. clef
16. bridle 17. meadow 18. fresco
19. accepted 20. tower

Part II

1. crave 2. high 3. diminish
4. annul 5. loot 6. hale 7. cringe
8. severable 9. kismet 10. premiss
11. lavish 12. capacity 13. serene
14. staff 15. dignitary 16. beatific
17. descendants 18. mediate
19. renunciation 20. bonus

Part III

1. lavish 2. eternal 3. ignore
4. extricate 5. bow 6. apathetic
7. bright 8. dissolve 9. divergent
10. rashly 11. worried
12. unfamiliar 13. optional
14. cheerful 15. plumb 16. allow
17. isolated 18. chaste
19. unrelated 20. similar

Part IV

1. arm 2. Japan 3. perihelion
4. bulwark 5. persecution 6. theft
7. roof 8. cancel
9. representatives 10. young
11. solicitous 12. engine
13. reluctant 14. nymphet
15. urbane 16. biscuit 17. sluggish
18. petals 19. wood 20. fish

Part V

1. rear, foster 2. juncture, moment
3. stereotype, pigeonhole
4. magnate, plutocrat 5. deity, idol
6. nothing, cipher 7. revere,
venerate 8. homespun, rustic
9. row, rank 10. mire, morass
11. vestige, remnant 12. salient,
important 13. convivial,
gregarious 14. zealot, fanatic
15. sidelong, oblique 16. omen,
presage 17. ulterior, covert
18. gourmet, epicure 19. fiat,
decree 20. obdurate, stubborn

Part VI

1. desert, rescue 2. similar, varying 3. minuscule, enormous 4. bloat, deflate 5. catty, pleasant 6. evasive, candid 7. adorable, obnoxious 8. unusual, traditional 9. totalitarian, democratic 10. slapdash, pernickety 11. taxing, effortless 12. ostentatious, modest 13. wrathful, contented 14. bias, tolerance 15. procrastinate, expedite 16. facilitate, frustrate 17. resilient, sensitive 18. fatal, innocuous 19. toxic, salubrious 20. worsen, ameliorate

Part VII

1. post 2. rest 3. tip 4. scale 5. date 6. tense 7. well 8. jam 9. angle 10. lie 11. recede 12. bay 13. retort 14. fallow 15. utter 16. wag 17. hobby 18. hob 19. bale 20. ouch

Part VIII

1. man 2. suit 3. book 4. some 5. way 6. it 7. pack 8. or 9. wood 10. on 11. son 12. can 13. ire 14. proof 15. ant 16. eye 17. ton 18. star 19. wit 20. us

Part IX

1. D 2. D 3. B 4. D 5. D 6. F 7. D 8. D 9. E 10. E

Part X

1. B (£0.60) 2. C 3. 21 (starting at 1 and working clockwise, move two segments adding 1, then 2, then 3, etc) 4. C (20 mins) 5. B 6. E (minus £50) 7. D (6.4 miles) 8. C (3 mins) 9. 124 ($+ 1 \times 1 + 2 \times 2 + 3 \times 3 + 4 \times 4$) 10. $3\frac{1}{2}$

✳ TOTAL SCORE ✳	
80 - 100	AVERAGE
101 - 130	GOOD
131 - 160	VERY GOOD
161 - 200	EXCEPTIONAL

TEST THREE

Test Three

Part I is a series of 20 questions designed to test your ability in collecting together objects or ideas that belong to a set or that have some common attribute. To make this classification simpler we have put together a series of words, and you have to spot the 'odd one out'. There are five words and only four of them have a common theme; underline the <u>odd one</u>.

Example: bag, basket, <u>hat</u>, pocket, bucket
Answer: <u>hat</u>, the other four are used for carrying things

You have 10 minutes to complete the 20 questions.

Each correct answer scores one point.

8 - 10	AVERAGE
11 - 13	GOOD
14 - 16	VERY GOOD
17 - 20	EXCEPTIONAL

1. clink, can, stage, stir, jug
2. caitiff, paragon, miscreant, villain, rascal
3. adjudicator, jocose, arbiter, referee, umpire
4. macaw, toucan, cougar, wagtail, buzzard
5. nadir, zenith, apogee, apex, pinnacle
6. contumacious, obsequious, sycophantic, servile, deferential
7. petronel, rapier, stylet, tulwar, cutlass
8. maharajah, pasha, martinet, nabob, bey
9. accelerando, atonal, anatto, arioso, animato
10. bondage, thraldom, vassalage, servitude, obfuscation
11. amphitheatre, hippodrome, stadium, playhouse, arbalest
12. gloxinia, clarkia, calendula, deodar, narcissus
13. centipede, mantis, millepede, tarantula, samoyed
14. Constable, Dali, Eyck, Gauguin, Gladstone
15. schooner, felucca, galliot, scauper, caravel
16. vendor, dacoit, brigand, bandit, freebooter
17. careless, lackadaisical, feckless, listless, predilection
18. sepia, auburn, hazel, chestnut, cobalt
19. Campari, Pernod, Chablis, Graves, Bergen
20. battledore, sculling, dominoes, ouzel, hurdling

Test Three

Part II is a series of 20 questions designed to test your knowledge of language and your ability to spot words that have the same meaning. We have grouped together five words, and from them you have to underline the <u>word</u> that means the same as or has the closest meaning to the KEY word.

Example: ANGULAR (blunt, stiff, abrupt, <u>branching</u>, cornered)

Answer: <u>branching</u> is the word closest in meaning to the KEY word, ANGULAR

You have 10 minutes to complete the 20 questions.

Each correct answer scores one point.

8 - 10	AVERAGE
11 - 13	GOOD
14 - 16	VERY GOOD
17 - 20	EXCEPTIONAL

1. SATURNINE (robust, gloomy, rotund, showy, beneficial)
2. HALCYON (rough, calm, angry, exciting, pleasurable)
3. GIMCRACK (knickknack, jewel, joke, treadmill, pastiche)
4. DRACONIAN (lenient, stupid, severe, easy, lazy)
5. INSOLVENT (sticky, pure, depressed, mystified, bankrupt)
6. EERIE (nest, weird, early, safe, misty)
7. PROPENSITY (spectacle, disposition, personal, dejection, stoutness)
8. CONDUIT (banner, show, duct, pitch, summit)
9. ENLARGE (refresh, maintain, oppose, dilate, provide)
10. SALUBRIOUS (flippant, morose, healthy, cruel, economical)
11. REPUGN (reply, oppose, hate, support, praise)
12. VENAL (bloody, corrupt, urgent, sensual, decorous)
13. FOSSE (ditch, hill, valley, slope, stream)
14. PIED (variegated, striped, uniform, edible, coloured)
15. PUSILLANIMOUS (oscillating, cowardly, threatening, pulsating, briskly)
16. KNOLL (bole, valley, hillock, outcrop, niche)
17. NOCTAMBULIST (sleep-walker, tight-rope walker, fire-walker, jay-walker, fakir)
18. SORREL (reddish-brown, grey, silver, fawn, reddish-purple)
19. LIMPID (lucid, sloppy, sharp, ancient, impure)
20. WRAITH (phantom, anger, solace, remedy, brilliance)

Test Three

Part III is a series of 20 questions designed to test your knowledge of language and your ability to visualize opposite meanings quickly. We have grouped together five words and from them you have to underline the <u>word</u> that means the opposite or is as nearly as possible opposite in meaning to the KEY word.

Example: CARELESS (exact, <u>heedful</u>, strict, anxious, dutiful)
Answer: <u>heedful</u> is the word that means the opposite of the
KEY word CARELESS

You have 10 minutes to complete the 20 questions.

Each correct answer scores one point.

8 - 10	AVERAGE
11 - 13	GOOD
14 - 16	VERY GOOD
17 - 20	EXCEPTIONAL

1. NUGATORY (valuable, worthless, rocklike, slender, voluptuous)
2. PALTRY (mean, trashy, worthwhile, strong, bitter)
3. EVANESCENCE (appearance, vanishing, floating, discovery, rosy)
4. EDACIOUS (gluttonous, fasting, full, even, smart)
5. DOLEFUL (happy, gloomy, poor, rich, steady)
6. LAVISH (unrestrained, meagre, profuse, waste, prodigious)
7. CRASS (dense, coarse, refined, gross, manly)
8. REVERE (respect, reverse, disdain, praise, procure)
9. COSSET (neglect, pamper, shine, divert, pinch)
10. ELATED (pampered, lengthened, proud, dejected, concise)
11. ARID (parched, dried, deserted, watchful, soaked)
12. SEDATE (calm, excited, imprisoned, released, proclaim)
13. CAPITULATE (hoard, venerate, destroy, conquer, surrender)
14. ADMONISH (deduce, censure, reprove, praise, wilt)
15. MUNICIPAL (citidel, wealthy, rustic, bloated, kind)
16. MUTE (noisy, silent, dumb, discordant, proven)
17. MORBID (healthy, discarded, sickly, upright, clever)
18. EMANCIPATE (release, fine, acclaim, reward, imprison)
19. LEGATO (smooth, uneven, lissom, brief, silent)
20. FULIGINOUS (red, black, white, dusky, blue)

Test Three

Part IV is a series of 20 questions designed to test your ability to visualize relationships between various objects and ideas. We have grouped together five words, one of which will pair up with the KEY word to produce a similar relationship to the two-word example. Underline the <u>word</u> that is appropriate.

Example: TIRED is to work as
HAPPY is to (sleep, rest, <u>success</u>, exercise, eating)

Answer: <u>success</u> has a similar relationship to HAPPY as work has to TIRED

You have 10 minutes to complete the 20 questions.

Each correct answer scores one point.

8 - 10 AVERAGE   11 - 13 GOOD
14 - 16 VERY GOOD   17 - 20 EXCEPTIONAL

ANALOGY

1. FISH is to barracuda as
   MAMMAL is to (thrasher, ruff, manatee, kelp, isopod)
2. PLATEAU is to tableland as
   POLDER is to (city, oasis, desert, reclaimed land, mountains)
3. INDIA is to rupee as
   NORWAY is to (kip, kyat, krone, krona, kwanga)
4. LUNAR is to moon as
   SIDEREAL is to (stars, planets, sun, meteors, comets)

5. JUNIPER is to shrub as
   FRAXINUS is to (tree, vegetable, fruit, flower, weed)
6. MELBA is to toast as
   FLAMBE is to (boiling water, petrol, brandy, cocktail, beer)
7. GINGHAM is to cotton as
   ASTRAKHAN is to (rabbit, lamb, cony, beaver, fox)
8. NETBALL is to basket as
   PELOTA is to (wall, net, posts, stumps, hoops)
9. CRIMSON is to red as
   GAMBOGE is to (pink, yellow, purple, mauve, green)
10. VENEER is to wood as
    STUCCO is to (paper, glue, plaster, glass, granite)
11. URBAN is to town as
    BUCOLIC is to (rustic, hills, seas, rivers, deserts)
12. CONVOLUTED is to rolled as
    SERRATED is to (notched, pinched, straight, curved, angled)
13. EULOGY is to praise as
    DEFAMATION is to (slander, libel, honesty, strength, idiocy)
14. CONFECTION is to sweets as
    BANE is to (poison, medicine, nectar, refreshment, oil)
15. IMPRESARIO is to manager as
    CHARLATAN is to (chief, clown, impostor, juggler, friend)
16. HOME is to base as
    REFUGE is to (sanctuary, dump, absentee, law, tip)
17. ARM is to humerus as
    LEG is to (femur, scapula, ulna, radius, carsus)
18. MISTRAL is to wind as
    MAELSTROM is to (hurricane, tornado, whirlpool, storm,
    drought)
19. PALMISTRY is to fortune telling as
    CALLIGRAPHY is to (pottery, painting, writing, singing, whistling)
20. LIBRETTO is to ORATORIO as
    CLERIHEW is to (poem, race, dance, jig, church)

Test Three

Part V is a series of 20 questions designed to test your knowledge of language and your ability to recognize words of similar meanings quickly. There are six words in each question and you have to find a pair of words that have similar meanings. Underline the two words that you believe to be closest in meaning.

Example: walk, run, drive, stroll, fly, sit

Answer: walk and stroll are the two words that are closest in meaning

You have 10 minutes to complete the 20 questions.

Each correct answer scores one point.

8 - 10	AVERAGE
11 - 13	GOOD
14 - 16	VERY GOOD
17 - 20	EXCEPTIONAL

1. perverse, clever, obstinate, defeated, defective, real
2. vagabond, misdemeanant, felon, whelp, castaway, jade
3. osteopath, optician, masseur, nurse, warden, bonesetter
4. brazen, frigid, indifferent, corpulent, rusty, simple
5. parsimonious, frugal, religious, hurtful, manly, divided
6. chattel, demesne, heritage, pitch, domain, claim
7. wrongdoer, wrangler, minister, songster, disc, debater
8. sycophant, grotesque, distorted, malingerer, besom, pecan
9. lawful, warranted, licit, equitable, illicit, chance
10. limit, item, emmet, insect, passion, strength
11. bishop, sorcerer, warlock, general, guard, battle
12. tippler, faster, huckster, bibber, glutton, servant
13. frolic, harry, hurry, badger, bodger, frenzy
14. cinnabar, florid, visage, countenance, glaucous, damask
15. claim, illiterate, verity, ignoramus, unqualified, inform
16. submission, objection, obeisance, depression, obstruction, occurrence
17. sound, persecute, corrosive, impeccable, deleterious, unblemished
18. moral, immoral, immortal, heavenly, perpetual, cautious
19. winsome, chicanery, endowment, fair, knavery, adroitness
20. applause, fulminate, plaudits, impeach, bewail, lampoon

Part VI is a series of 20 questions designed to test your knowledge of language and your ability to recognize words of opposite meanings quickly. There are six words in each question and you have to find a pair of words that have opposite meanings. Underline the <u>two words</u> that you believe to be opposite in meaning.

Example: curved, long, <u>big</u>, <u>small</u>, broad, fat

Answer: <u>big</u> and <u>small</u> are the two words in the list that are opposite in meaning

You have 10 minutes to complete the 20 questions.

Each correct answer scores one point.

8 - 10	AVERAGE
11 - 13	GOOD
14 - 16	VERY GOOD
17 - 20	EXCEPTIONAL

1. disbelief, medicated, fragile, odorous, fragrant, sturdy
2. impartial, repugnance, continuity, divested, vanquished, interested
3. narration, noxious, present, unharmful, drowning, distinct
4. diminished, felt, pardoned, increased, blessed, sounded
5. sensitive, irrigate, divide, transact, deem, drain
6. blocked, cute, empty, idiotic, connected, bustling
7. thankful, conflict, degenerate, peace, boredom, ecstacy
8. denoting, veering, slightly, backing, source, upright
9. mendacious, sagacious, active, proficient, capable, foolish
10. manifold, restricted, pristine, parasitic, conscious, contemporary
11. nitid, dull, blue, opaque, skimpy, determined
12. boastful, gelid, torrid, frightening, fearsome, marginal
13. gloaming, midday, tomorrow, monthly, atmosphere, dawn
14. involve, graduate, verity, canard, cloister, division
15. clinch, covetous, batch, digress, assent, undesired
16. probity, faceless, impecunious, real, fine, dishonour
17. tranquil, conception, accustomed, stormy, starry, powerful
18. special, soloist, paltry, novice, expert, exponent
19. infernal, heavenly, watchful, precocious, pendant, boastful
20. righteous, lepid, certain, unpleasant, composed, afraid

Test Three
PART VII

Part VII is a series of 20 questions designed to test your ability to find alternative meanings of words quickly You are looking for a word that has the same meaning as one word or phrase in one sense and the same meaning as a different word or phrase in another sense. The dots represent the number of letters in the missing word. Fill in the missing word.

Example: breathes heavily . . . . . underclothes
Answer: pants

You have 20 minutes to complete the 20 questions.

Each correct answer scores one point.

8 - 10	AVERAGE
11 - 13	GOOD
14 - 16	VERY GOOD
17 - 20	EXCEPTIONAL

DOUBLE MEANINGS

1. piece of pasteboard .... a wag
2. window frame .... turban cloth
3. mechanical memory .... medieval stringed instrument
4. a silvery fish ..... part of a sail
5. a short line .... rush
6. flat-bottomed boat .... to kick
7. a sea margin ...... twisted yarn
8. a chess piece .... to pledge
9. holly .... an islet
10. a boat fastener .... an artist
11. the right-hand side ...... breed of cattle
12. Indian crocodile ...... an attacker
13. hybrid rose .... small parcel of meat
14. void .... a sickly person
15. a Chinese official .... orange-like fruit
16. a beam ... a large fish
17. a seed vessel ... a small herd of whales
18. a large boat ...... to hurl
19. water-nymph ..... a dragonfly
20. variety of polecat ...... to search out

Test Three

Part VIII is a series of 20 questions designed to test your ability at innovation. You are given the first part of the word or phrase, and you have to find the second part. The same second part then becomes the first part of a second word or phrase. The dots represent the number of letters in the missing word. Fill in the missing word.

Example: house . . . . all
Answer: hold

You have 20 minutes to complete the 20 questions.

Each correct answer scores one point.

8 - 10	AVERAGE
11 - 13	GOOD
14 - 16	VERY GOOD
17 - 20	EXCEPTIONAL

DOUBLE WORDS

1. mid ..... light
2. school ...... mind
3. high .... locked
4. cart ..... box
5. half .... bodied
6. gad ... fishing
7. life ...... ship
8. clove ..... hiker
9. safety ..... class
10. thumb ..... ball
11. cuttle .... fingers
12. splash .... bone
13. fire ...... route
14. green ..... hold
15. rain ... fronted
16. charge .... shake
17. corn ...... stall
18. rising .... course
19. daisy ..... barrow
20. faint ..... beat

Test Three

Part IX is a series of 10 culture-free tests designed to test your powers of logical reasoning and understanding of relationships, pattern and design. Study each display of diagrams and select the missing item from the choices given. Study the instructions given to each question.

Example: Which is the odd one out?

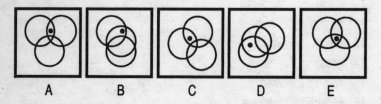

A   B   C   D   E

Answer: E – the dot is in three circles. In the other options it is in only two.

Each correct answer scores two points.

8 - 10	AVERAGE
12 - 14	GOOD
16	VERY GOOD
18 - 20	EXCEPTIONAL

1.

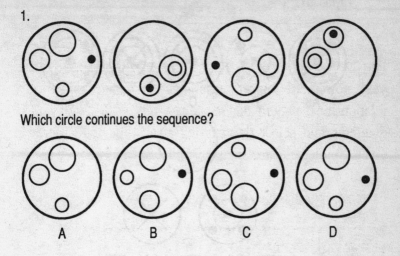

Which circle continues the sequence?

2. Which is the odd one out?

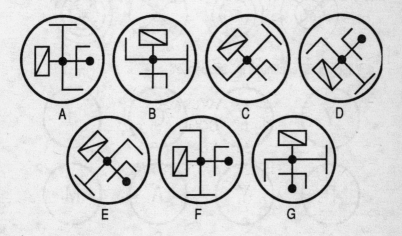

3. Which one of the following fits into the blank circle at the top of the pyramid?

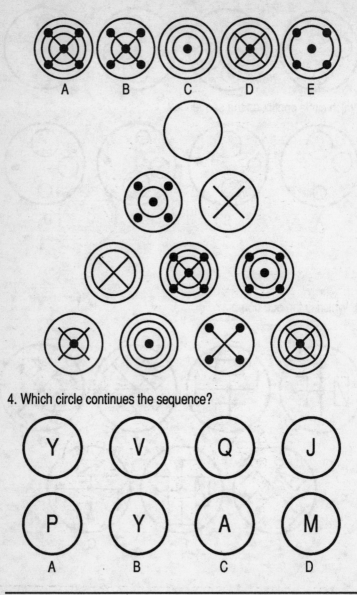

A   B   C   D   E

4. Which circle continues the sequence?

Y   V   Q   J

P   Y   A   M

A   B   C   D

5.

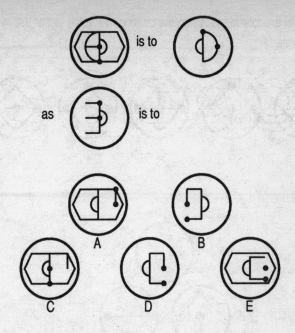

6. Which is the odd one out?

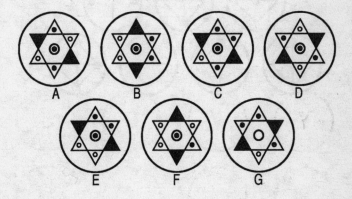

7. Which of the following fits into the blank circle at the top of the
   pyramid?

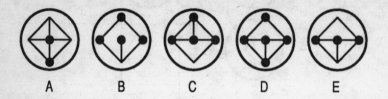

A B C D E

8. Find the missing tile

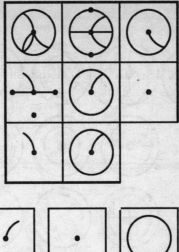

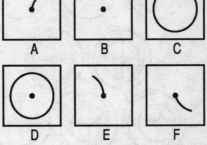

9. Which is the odd one out?

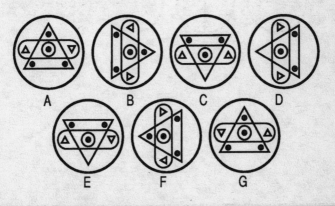

10. Find the missing circle.

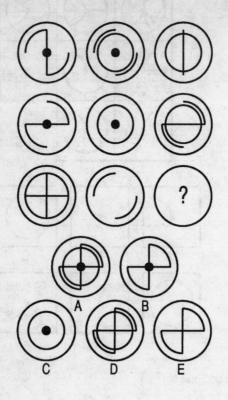

Test Three

Part X is a series of 10 tests designed to test your powers of calculation and logic. From the alternatives given in each question choose the answer that you think is correct.

Example: My watch shows the time at 12.25; one clock shows 12.10. The radio announces 12.30, the church clock strikes 12.00, and your watch shows 12.15. The correct time is 12.20. What is the average time, fast or slow, as shown by these timepieces?

A. 2 mins slow   B. 4 mins slow   C. 6 mins slow
D. 2 mins fast   E. 4 mins fast   F. 6 mins fast

Answer: B. 4 mins slow

You have 20 minutes in which to solve the 10 questions.

Each correct answer scores two points.

8 - 10	AVERAGE
12 - 14	GOOD
16	VERY GOOD
18 - 20	EXCEPTIONAL

1. A boy has as many sisters as brothers, but each sister has only half as many sisters as brothers. How many sisters and brothers are there in the family?

   A. 4 brothers and 6 sisters
   B. 6 brothers and 4 sisters
   C. 3 brothers and 4 sisters
   D. 4 brothers and 3 sisters

2. 'How heavy is this bag of cement?' asked the builder. The salesman replied: '512lb divided by half its own weight.'
   How heavy is the bag?

   A. 21lb   B. 102lb   C. 32lb   D. 40lb

3. If   62 = 86
   And   41 = 56
   What does 26 = ?

   A. 29   B. 30   C. 35   D. 40

4. In how many ways can a committee of seven be seated at a round table?

   A. 620   B. 640   C. 660   D. 680   E. 700   F. 720

5. What value weight would be required to balance the scales?

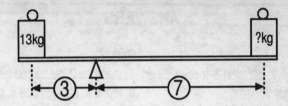

A. 5⁴/₇kg   B. 5⁵/₇kg   C. 5⁶/₇kg   D. 6kg   E. 6¹/₇kg   F. 6²/₇kg

6. What number comes next in the sequence 216, 125, 64, 27, X?

A. 5   B. 6   C. 7   D. 8   E. 9   F. 10

7. How many packets measuring 75 x 150 x 200mm can be packed
   into a box measuring 1.5 x 1.5 x 1m?

A. 1000   B. 500   C. 2000   D. 750

8. There are eight competitors in a race. In how many different ways
   can the first three places be formed?

A. 56   B. 72   C. 144   D. 168   E. 336

9. What fraction produces the recurring decimal .261261?

A. $^{26}/_{99}$ B. $^{261}/_{999}$ C. $^{261}/_{1000}$ D. $^{261261}/_{1000000}$

10. I have six shoes of three styles, and 24 socks, half of which are
    black and half of which are brown. How many shoes and socks
    must I select in the dark to have a matching pair of socks and a
    matching pair of shoes?

A. 3 socks and 3 shoes   B. 4 socks and 4 shoes
C. 3 socks and 4 shoes   D. 4 socks and 3 shoes

Test Three
ANSWERS

Part I
1. stage 2. paragon 3. jocose
4. cougar 5. nadir
6. contumacious 7. petronel
8. martinet 9. anatto
10. obfuscation 11. arbalest
12. deodar 13. samoyed
14. Gladstone 15. scauper
16. vendor 17. predilection
18. cobalt 19. Bergen 20. ouzel

Part II
1. gloomy 2. calm 3. knickknack
4. severe 5. bankrupt 6. weird
7. disposition 8. duct 9. dilate
10. healthy 11. oppose 12. corrupt
13. ditch 14. variegated
15. cowardly 16. hillock 17. sleep-
walker 18. reddish-brown 19. lucid
20. phantom

Part III
1. valuable 2. worthwhile
3. appearance 4. fasting 5. happy
6. meagre 7. refined 8. disdain
9. neglect 10. dejected
11. soaked 12. excited
13. conquer 14. praise 15. rustic
16. noisy 17. healthy 18. imprison
19. uneven 20. white

Part IV
1. manatee 2. reclaimed land
3. krone 4. stars 5. tree 6. brandy
7. lamb 8. wall 9. yellow
10. plaster 11. rustic 12. notched
13. slander 14. poison
15. impostor 16. sanctuary
17. femur 18. whirlpool 19. writing
20. poem

Part V
1. perverse, obstinate
2. misdemeanant, felon
3. osteopath, bonesetter 4. frigid,
indifferent 5. parsimonious, frugal
6. demesne, domain 7. wrangler,
debater 8. grotesque, distorted
9. lawful, licit 10. emmet, insect
11. sorcerer, warlock 12. tippler,
bibber 13. harry, badger
14. visage, countenance
15. illiterate, ignoramus
16. submission, obeisance
17. impeccable, unblemished
18. immortal, perpetual
19. chicanery, knavery
20. applause, plaudits

Part VI

1. fragile, sturdy 2. impartial, interested 3. noxious, unharmful 4. diminished, increased 5. irrigate, drain 6. cute, idiotic 7. conflict, peace 8. veering, backing 9. sagacious, foolish 10. pristine, contemporary 11. nitid, dull 12. gelid, torrid 13. gloaming, dawn 14. verity, canard 15. covetous, undesired 16. probity, dishonour 17. tranquil, stormy 18. novice, expert 19. infernal, heavenly 20. lepid, unpleasant

Part VII

1. card 2. sash 3. rote 4. roach 5. dash 6. punt 7. strand 8. pawn 9. holm 10. painter 11. dexter 12. mugger 13. noisette 14. invalid 15. mandarin 16. ray 17. pod 18. launch 19. naiad 20. ferret

Part VIII

1. night 2. master 3. land 4. horse 5. full 6. fly 7. rocket 8. hitch 9. first 10. screw 11. fish 12. back 13. escape 14. house 15. bow 16. hand 17. flower 18. damp 19. wheel 20. heart

Part IX

1. D 2. E 3. B 4. C 5. E 6. F 7. E 8. B 9. E 10. E

Part X

1. D 2. C. 32lb 3. C 35 4. F 720 5. A 5^4/$_7$kg 6. D 8 7. A 1000 8. 336 9. ^{261}/$_{999}$ 10. C

✳ TOTAL SCORE ✳	
80 - 100	AVERAGE
101 - 130	GOOD
131 - 160	VERY GOOD
161 - 200	EXCEPTIONAL

TEST FOUR

Test Four

PART I

Part I is a series of 20 questions designed to test your ability in collecting together objects or ideas that belong to a set or that have some common attribute. To make this classification simpler we have put together a series of words, and you have to spot the 'odd one out'. There are five words and only four of them have a common theme; underline the odd one.

Example: bag, basket, hat, pocket, bucket
Answer: hat, the other four are used for carrying things

You have 10 minutes to complete the 20 questions.

Each correct answer scores one point.

8 - 10	AVERAGE
11 - 13	GOOD
14 - 16	VERY GOOD
17 - 20	EXCEPTIONAL

1. breakwater, groyne, bulwark, buffer, lumber
2. stoup, bethel, tabernacle, kirk, church
3. sorcerer, hierarchy, magician, necromancer, seer
4. laconic, labyrinthine, intricate, perplexing, entangling
5. vacillate, fluctuate, oscillate, hesitate, primate
6. quagmire, morass, slough, swamp, miasma
7. sombrero, panama, cravat, tam-o'-shanter, bonnet
8. dinar, rouble, glottis, punt, sucre
9. shimmy, carousel, turkey-trot, cakewalk, polka
10. strontuim, salpinctes, titanium, lithium, tungsten
11. rake, minx, jade, trollop, hussy
12. beta, forint, sigma, delta, kappa
13. cornelian, jasper, blazon, beryl, agate
14. maple, rubber, coconut, hornbeam, petunia
15. nephritis, sciatica, phlebitis, chiasmus, glaucoma
16. tumbrel, hansom, bucentaur, landaulet, britzka
17. corncrake, chiffchaff, grampus, parakeet, dotterel
18. Crete, Pearl, Sumatra, Vancouver, Caspian
19. vermilion, carmine, malachite, cerise, maroon
20. percolator, gridiron, porringer, liquidizer, chicane

Test Four

Part II is a series of 20 questions designed to test your knowledge of language and your ability to spot words that have the same meaning. We have grouped together five words, and from them you have to underline the <u>word</u> that means the same as or has the closest meaning to the KEY word.

Example: ANGULAR (blunt, stiff, abrupt, <u>branching</u>, cornered)

Answer: <u>branching</u> is the word closest in meaning to the KEY word, ANGULAR

You have 10 minutes to complete the 20 questions.

Each correct answer scores one point.

8 - 10	AVERAGE
11 - 13	GOOD
14 - 16	VERY GOOD
17 - 20	EXCEPTIONAL

1. MAWKISH (silly, foolish, disgusting, clever, crooked)
2. CALUMNY (district, lust, slander, quickness, fraud)
3. FERAL (wild, iron, rapid, hated, clan)
4. GRANDEUR (lord, mansion, splendour, benevolent, beneficial)
5. HOODWINK (tether, ogle, headgear, flirt, blindfold)
6. KNELL (profit, charm, toll, fate, forecast)
7. NACARAT (orange-red, red-mauve, blue-puce, pink-brown, yellow-red)
8. NUNCIO (messenger, administrator, hermit, official, madman)
9. GRIFF (claw, nail, bone, muscle, ligament)
10. APOSTATE (gallant, coxcomb, herald, renegade, saint)
11. SALLY (incursion, fair-ground, joker, fool, moppet)
12. FILLIP (standard, temper, consume, stimulus, over-fill)
13. FLORID (ornate, shadowy, burnt, infamous, insipid)
14. KAMPONG (valley, forest, river, hill, village)
15. MISSIVE (rocket, epistle, mission, freedom, extreme)
16. JOCOSE (funny, ugly, sleepy, mischievous, balmy)
17. SUAVE (bland, ruthless, criminal, hairy, smart)
18. EREMITE (recluse, habit, twilight, dwelling, gelding)
19. TURBID (swollen, muddy, deep, thoughtful, determined)
20. CAVEAT (bagatelle, bauble, animosity, force, warning)

Part III is a series of 20 questions designed to test your knowledge of language and your ability to visualize opposite meanings quickly. We have grouped together five words and from them you have to underline the <u>word</u> that means the opposite or is as nearly as possible opposite in meaning to the KEY word.

Example: CARELESS (exact, <u>heedful</u>, strict, anxious, dutiful)
Answer: <u>heedful</u> is the word that means the opposite of the
          KEY word CARELESS

You have 10 minutes to complete the 20 questions.

Each correct answer scores one point.

8 - 10	AVERAGE
11 - 13	GOOD
14 - 16	VERY GOOD
17 - 20	EXCEPTIONAL

1. ARCHAIC (modern, old, dilapidated, crenellated, broken)
2. CAUTIOUS (wary, impulsive, circumspect, gregarious, baleful)
3. LUCENT (shining, dull, bright, ringing, majestic)
4. FUGACIOUS (stationary, volatile, voluptuous, skinny, puerile)
5. SALLOW (yellowish, plain, ruddy, sickly, dark)
6. ALLURE (entice, decoy, repulse, notice, develop)
7. INHIBIT (waver, prohibit, release, restrain, influence)
8. PIQUANCY (sharpness, dullness, rosy, lively, solid)
9. EGREGIOUS (prominent, subdued, welcoming, hated, charming)
10. BROACH (join, split, weave, produce, summon)
11. FALLIBLE (unmistaken, wary, mistaken, unwary, full)
12. CONFEDERATE (club, ally, enemy, friend, partner)
13. DERIDE (unseat, ridicule, praise, steady, jump)
14. LEGIBLE (unreadable, legal, unlawful, readable, stern)
15. CONCORD (powerful, discord, harmony, bravery, cowardice)
16. METICULOUS (painstaking, efficient, drab, sloppy, neat)
17. BATED (diminished, increased, lessened, crossed, sized)
18. EMACIATE (slim, fatten, weaken, display, dispose)
19. DURGAN (giant, dwarf, witch, magician, fairy)
20. COUTH (balanced, slovenly, sophisticated, pristine, fit)

Test Four

Part IV is a series of 20 questions designed to test your ability to visualize relationships between various objects and ideas. We have grouped together five words, one of which will pair up with the KEY word to produce a similar relationship to the two-word example. Underline the <u>word</u> that is appropriate.

Example: TIRED is to work as
HAPPY is to (sleep, rest, <u>success</u>, exercise, eating)

Answer: <u>success</u> has a similar relationship to HAPPY as work has to TIRED

You have 10 minutes to complete the 20 questions.

Each correct answer scores one point.

8 - 10 AVERAGE	11 - 13 GOOD
14 - 16 VERY GOOD	17 - 20 EXCEPTIONAL

ANALOGY

1. ANIMAL is to panther as
   BIRD is to (lemming, sorrel, tiercel, unicorn, capuchin)
2. TARANTULA is to spider as
   BOMBARDIER is to (beetle, ant, worm, butterfly, frog)
3. WOODWIND is to clarinet as
   PERCUSSION is to (viola, flute, cymbals, violins, trombone)
4. DECIDUOUS is to willow as
   CONIFEROUS is to (oak, elm, spruce, ash, lime)

5. HEAD is to cranium as
   KNEE is to (patella, tarsus, lumber, coccyx, phalanges)
6. GEESE are to gaggle as
   CROWS are to (trip, murmur, murder, skein, flock)
7. PUCE is to brownish-purple as
   SANGUINE is to (red, green, yellow, blue, orange)
8. CHORUS is to song as
   ACT is to (play, script, producer, scenery, stage)
9. CRUCIFORM is to cross as
   ALATED is to (shield, wing, tapered, branching, curved)
10. ROAD is to camber as
    RAMP is to (concrete, high, slope, low, level)
11. IGLOO is to ice as
    MARQUEE is to (buckram, canvas, silk, sateen, worsted)
12. MERINGUE is to eggs as
    FRICANDEAU is to (chicken, pork, veal, lamb, beef)
13. METHEGLIN is to mead as
    AMONTILLADO is to (rum, whisky, sherry, gin, vodka)
14. NOVICE is to learner as
    HARBINGER is to (robber, pickpocket, thief, tradesman,
    messenger)
15. ESTONIA is to rouble as
    CHILE is to (peso, dinar, cordeba, peseta, franc)
16. FINBACK is to whale as
    GOOSANDER is to (behemoth, sawbill, lizard, chamois, gazelle)
17. RESISTANCE is to ohms as
    CURRENT is to (watts, volts, amperes, litres, joules)
18. ARQUEBUS is to musket as
    BASINET is to (spear, breastplate, helmet, leggings, gauntlet)
19. JESTER is to fool as
    LARRIKIN is to (saint, hooligan, musician, dancer, leader)
20. VOID is to emptiness as
    PLETHORA is to (stability, sameness, fallow, glut, scarcity)

Test Four

Part V is a series of 20 questions designed to test your knowledge of language and your ability to recognize words of similar meanings quickly. There are six words in each question and you have to find a pair of words that have similar meanings. Underline the <u>two words</u> that you believe to be closest in meaning.

Example: <u>walk</u>, run, drive, <u>stroll</u>, fly, sit
Answer: <u>walk</u> and <u>stroll</u> are the two words that are closest in meaning

You have 10 minutes to complete the 20 questions.

Each correct answer scores one point.

8 - 10	AVERAGE
11 - 13	GOOD
14 - 16	VERY GOOD
17 - 20	EXCEPTIONAL

1. actors, hustings, circus, stage, patchwork, denizen
2. belladonna, poplar, nightshade, petunia, orchard, pannier
3. mundane, prostrate, vertical, horizontal, propensity, multifarious
4. archaic, puritanical, rude, malignant, beaten, prudish
5. prison, bailiwick, shrievalty, castle, church, windmill
6. fiend, hostler, mogul, tycoon, caliph, liegeman
7. dogma, pet, igloo, homestead, length, tenet
8. erudition, malpractice, suicidal, bonny, leaning, learning
9. sanctify, unjust, sacrilege, hallow, bigoted, brave
10. pasture, chattels, warmth, goods, epics, realm
11. terrorize, servile, obsequious, intimate, inimical, parasite
12. lineage, linear, ancestry, ancient, destiny, summit
13. flexion, digress, baste, wander, blemish, sound
14. general, occidental, Eastern, Western, peninsula, likeness
15. balance, reparation, reward, compensation, loss, bemused
16. stance, mountebank, hyperbole, pantomime, exaggeration, exponent
17. mobile, memento, blighted, masterly, insidious, mercurial
18. promptitude, perpetrate, alacrity, proceed, profane, imagine
19. hieroglyphics, tablet, chisel, representation, pyramid, stencil
20. exorcist, cabel, amulet, talisman, rectorship, druid

Test Four

PART VI

Part VI is a series of 20 questions designed to test your knowledge of language and your ability to recognize words of opposite meanings quickly. There are six words in each question and you have to find a pair of words that have opposite meanings. Underline the <u>two words</u> that you believe to be opposite in meaning.

Example: curved, long, <u>big</u>, <u>small</u>, broad, fat

Answer   <u>big</u> and <u>small</u> are the two words in the list that are opposite in meaning

You have 10 minutes to complete the 20 questions.

Each correct answer scores one point.

8 - 10	AVERAGE
11 - 13	GOOD
14 - 16	VERY GOOD
17 - 20	EXCEPTIONAL

1. scattered, diffident, comprising, boastful, articles, watchful
2. cloister, repugnance, brazen, affection, secret, changed
3. profit, potent, detachable, emulation, insipid, character
4. gloom, sardonic, gamine, crone, effigy, romantic
5. irritate, defect, defend, perfection, procrastinate, sympathy
6. philander, purist, prim, informal, purport, inapt
7. encourage, groggy, rubbing, sober, listening, horror
8. doctrine, salve, radical, irritate, contrive, periodical
9. banal, kind, early, special, presumptuous, stripped
10. haugh, lock, hillock, waterfall, crevasse, coppice
11. emaciated, capable, notched, wealthy, emancipated, bloated
12. intricate, simple, benevolent, composed, fast, sweet
13. vassal, bodyguard, lethargic, principle, busy, escapement
14. desirous, prime, garrulous, exponential, dumb, equivocal
15. withershins, clockwise, confirmation, shoulders, flexible, safe
16. disperse, clandestine, chanced, public, solemn, mean
17. insignificant, derelict, taboo, subdued, ephemeral, permitted
18. metamorphosis, puerile, sinful, adult, concealed, revoked
19. vulnerable, lanceolate, blunted, triangular, rotund, blissful
20. grade, genuine, dismay, benefit, scoff, cheer

Part VII is a series of 20 questions designed to test your ability to find alternative meanings of words quickly You are looking for a word that has the same meaning as one word or phrase in one sense and the same meaning as a different word or phrase in another sense. The dots represent the number of letters in the missing word. Fill in the missing word.

Example: breathes heavily . . . . . underclothes
Answer: pants

You have 20 minutes to complete the 20 questions.

Each correct answer scores one point.

8 - 10	AVERAGE
11 - 13	GOOD
14 - 16	VERY GOOD
17 - 20	EXCEPTIONAL

DOUBLE MEANINGS

1. a sea fish .... low part in music
2. short, informal letter .... a young girl
3. row of bushes ..... be evasive
4. a mocking look .... a monocle
5. dish of pastry .... sharp
6. booty ...... impairs
7. compartment for bombs ... inlet of the sea
8. a newspaper ..... a non-resident servant
9. beaver's dwelling ..... to deposit
10. oily substance from milk ..... select the best
11. seek to influence ..... small hall
12. a limit ..... to spring
13. blond .... clear
14. two-wheeled carriage ... one night's performance
15. urgent entreaty .... lawsuit
16. to mark ...... to withdraw
17. strong ale ... tree nail
18. companion .... win at chess
19. swimming stroke ..... move slowly
20. moist air .... discourage

Test Four

Part VIII is a series of 20 questions designed to test your ability at innovation. You are given the first part of the word or phrase, and you have to find the second part. The same second part then becomes the first part of a second word or phrase. The dots represent the number of letters in the missing word. Fill in the missing word.

Example: house . . . . all
Answer: hold

You have 20 minutes to complete the 20 questions.

Each correct answer scores one point.

> 8 - 10   AVERAGE
> 11 - 13 GOOD
> 14 - 16 VERY GOOD
> 17 - 20 EXCEPTIONAL

1. trip . . . . . . toe
2. soft . . . . . paper
3. swine . . . . . few
4. sugar . . . . . floss
5. shop . . . . . . dresser
6. sealing . . . effigy
7. quick . . . . bunker
8. acid . . . . forest
9. dinner . . . . . glass
10. face . . . . . . room
11. stool . . . . . . toed
12. paper . . . . . sharpener
13. pillow . . . . history
14. water . . . . . cloth
15. wedding . . . break
16. bitter . . . . . heart
17. buffer . . . . . room
18. hunch . . . . gammon
19. corner . . . . . mason
20. counter . . . . football

Test Four

Part IX is a series of 10 culture-free tests designed to test your powers of logical reasoning and understanding of relationships, pattern and design. Study each display of diagrams and select the missing item from the choices given. Study the instructions given to each question.

Example: Which is the odd one out?

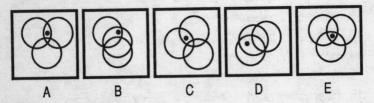

| A | B | C | D | E |

Answer: E – the dot is in three circles. In the other options it is in only two.

Each correct answer scores two points.

8 - 10	AVERAGE
12 - 14	GOOD
16	VERY GOOD
18 - 20	EXCEPTIONAL

1.

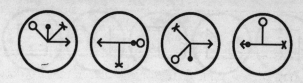

Which circle continues the sequence?

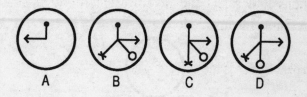

2. Which is the odd one out?

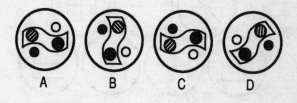

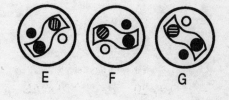

3. Which of the following fits into the blank circle at the top of the pyramid?

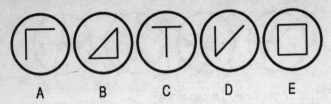

A   B   C   D   E

4.

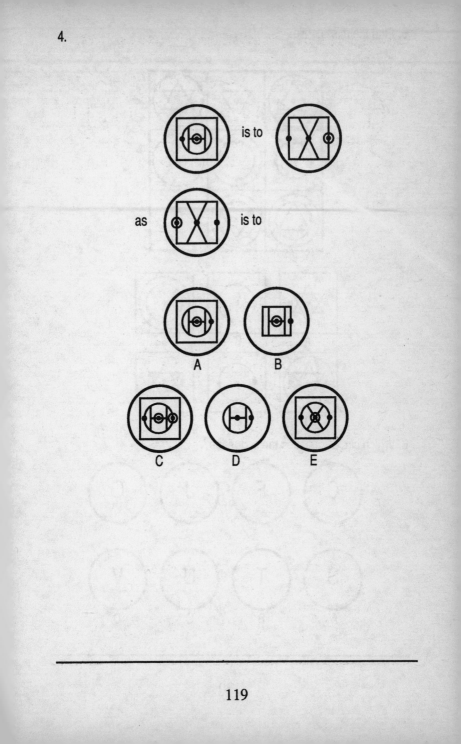

5. Find the missing tile.

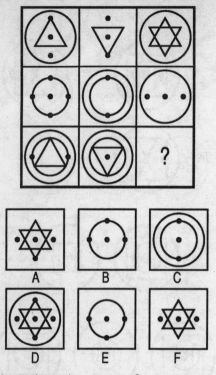

A   B   C

D   E   F

6. Which circle continues the sequence?

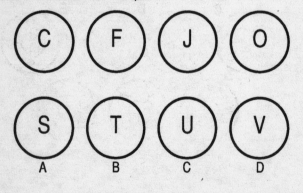

C   F   J   O

S   T   U   V

A   B   C   D

7. Find the missing circle.

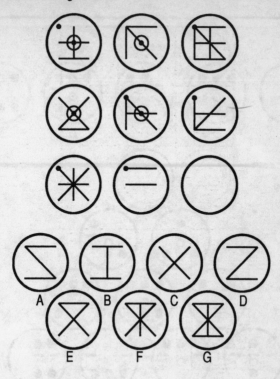

8. Which is the odd one out?

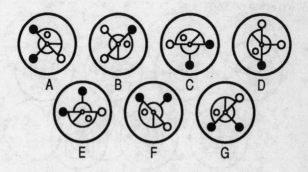

9. Which of the following fits into the blank circle at the top of the pyramid?

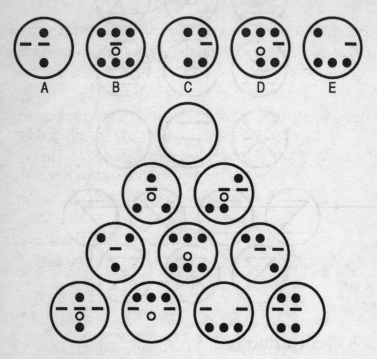

10. Which is the odd one out?

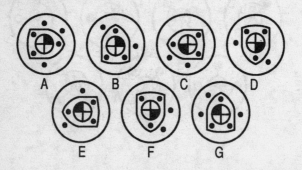

Test Four

Part X is a series of 10 tests designed to test your powers of calculation and logic. From the alternatives given in each question choose the answer that you think is correct.

Example: My watch shows the time at 12.25; one clock shows 12.10. The radio announces 12.30, the church clock strikes 12.00, and your watch shows 12.15. The correct time is 12.20. What is the average time, fast or slow, as shown by these timepieces?

A. 2 mins slow B. 4 mins slow C. 6 mins slow
D. 2 mins fast E. 4 mins fast F. 6 mins fast

Answer: B. 4 mins slow

You have 20 minutes in which to solve the 10 questions.

Each correct answer scores two points.

8 - 10	AVERAGE
12 - 14	GOOD
16	VERY GOOD
18 - 20	EXCEPTIONAL

1. An invention saves 30 per cent of fuel, a second invention saves 40 per cent of fuel, a third invention saves 20 per cent of fuel. If all three inventions are used at once on the same engine what percentage of fuel is saved?

A. 34   B. 50   C. 66   D. 78   E. 90

2. What is the missing number?

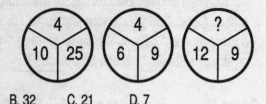

A. 16   B. 32   C. 21   D. 7

3. What are the chances of selecting the king of spades twice in two selections, one each from two standard packs of 52 cards?

A. $\frac{1}{2801}$ B. $\frac{1}{2604}$ C. $\frac{1}{2701}$ D. $\frac{1}{2704}$ E. $\frac{1}{2601}$

4. You are standing at the top of a church tower, and you drop a tennis ball over the parapet. The ball reaches the ground after 4 seconds. How high is the tower?

A. 250ft   B. 256ft   C. 262ft   D. 268ft   E. 274ft   F. 280ft

5. L T N H M

Which letter continues the above sequence?

E   F   Z   K

6. With one throw of a pair of eight-sided dice, each numbered 1 to 8, what are the chances out of a possible 64 combinations of throwing 12 or 13?

A. 7   B. 8   C. 9   D. 10   E. 11   F. 12

7. How many squares can be seen on an eight-by-eight chess board?

A. 184   B. 188   C. 192   D. 196   E. 200   F. 204

8. If ten window cleaners with ten cradles cleaned the windows on ten floors in ten hours, how long would it take five window cleaners with five cradles to clean the windows on five floors?

A. 2 hours   B. 5 hours   C. 7 hours   D. 10 hours

9. If 40 = 44 and 55 = 61, what does 47 = ?

A. 49   B. 50   C. 51   D. 52   E. 53

10. If you place all 28 dominoes in a chain so that five pips are on one end, how many pips will be on the other end?

A. 1   B. 2   C. 3   D. 4   E. 5   F. 6

Test Four

Part I

1. lumber 2. stoup 3. hierarchy
4. laconic 5. primate 6. miasma
7. cravat 8. glottis 9. carousel
10. salpinctes 11. rake 12. forint
13. blazon 14. petunia
15. chiasmus 16. bucentaur
17. grampus 18. Caspian
19. malachite 20. chicane

Part II

1. disgusting 2. slander 3. wild
4. splendour 5. blindfold 6. toll
7. orange-red 8. messenger
9. claw 10. renegade
11. incursion 12. stimulus
13. ornate 14. village 15. epistle
16. funny 17. bland 18. recluse
19. muddy 20. warning

Part III

1. modern 2. impulsive 3. dull
4. stationary 5. ruddy 6. repulse
7. release 8. dullness 9. subdued
10. join 11. unmistaken 12. enemy
13. praise 14. unreadable
15. discord 16. sloppy
17. increased 18. fatten 19. giant
20. slovenly

Part IV

1. tiercel 2. beetle 3. cymbals
4. spruce 5. patella 6. murder
7. red 8. play 9. wing 10. slope
11. canvas 12. veal 13. sherry
14. messenger 15. peso
16. sawbill 17. amperes
18. helmet 19. hooligan 20. glut

Part V

1. hustings, stage 2. belladonna,
nightshade 3. prostrate, horizontal
4. puritanical, prudish 5. bailiwick,
shrievalty 6. mogul, caliph
7. dogma, tenet 8. erudition,
learning 9. sanctify, hallow
10. chattels, goods 11. servile,
obsequious 12. lineage, ancestry
13. digress, wander
14. occidental, Western
15. reparation, compensation
16. hyperbole, exaggeration
17. mobile, mercurial
18. promptitude, alacrity
19. hieroglyphics, representation
20. amulet, talisman

Part VI

1. diffident, boastful
2. repugnance, affection
3. potent, insipid 4. gamine, crone
5. defect, perfection 6. prim, informal 7. groggy, sober 8. salve, irritate 9. banal, special
10. haugh, hillock 11. emaciated, bloated 12. intricate, simple
13. lethargic, busy 14. garrulous, dumb 15. withershins, clockwise
16. clandestine, public 17. taboo, permitted 18. puerile, adult
19. lanceolate, blunted 20. scoff, cheer

Part VII

1. bass 2. chit 3. hedge 4. quiz
5. tart 6. spoils 7. bay 8. daily
9. lodge 10. cream 11. lobby
12. bound 13. fair 14. gig 15. plea
16. scratch 17. nog 18. mate
19. crawl 20. damp

Part VIII

1. hammer 2. touch 3. fever
4. candy 5. window 6. wax 7. sand
8. rain 9. plate 10. powder
11. pigeon 12. knife 13. case
14. table 15. day 16. sweet
17. state 18. back 19. stone
20. blow

Part IX

1. B 2. F 3. D 4. A 5. F 6. C 7. F
8. F 9. C 10. D

Part X

1. C 66 2. A 16 3. E $^{1}/_{2601}$
4. B 256ft 5. E 6. C 9 7. F 204
8. D 10 hours 9. D 52 10. E 5

✳ TOTAL SCORE ✳

80 - 100	AVERAGE
101 - 130	GOOD
131 - 160	VERY GOOD
161 - 200	EXCEPTIONAL